The Hitch-Hiker's Guide to Heaven

Vic Jackopson

Marshalls

Dedication:

to my two daughters
Christy and Ruth

Marshalls Paperbacks
Marshall Morgan & Scott

3 Beggarwood Lane, Basingstoke, Hants. RG23 7LP

First published by Marshall Morgan & Scott 1983

ISBN 0 551 00954 3

Printed in Great Britain by
Richard Clay (The Chaucer Press) Ltd,
Bungay, Suffolk

Contents

Preface

My ambition in writing this short novel was at first to communicate to you, my reader, a clean presentation of the main passage of the Bible in simple easy to understand language and situations. As I continued writing I found Tom taking over my humble attempts at fiction, and developing the beginnings of a training manual for you to pass on to others what you have learned.

If you are without faith right now I hope and pray that you will, through these words, discover the way to real life with Christ as your Saviour. When you have finished reading you can pass the book on to someone else. Who knows where it might end?

I would like to acknowledge my indebtedness to my friend, Archie Parrish, who first planted the seed thought in my mind for this book, and to my dear Sue, without whose encouragement you would not be reading this now.

Vic Jackopson
Southampton 1983.

1
A damp November morning

Come on, you ----! I'll never make it to court on time if I don't get a lift!

A container lorry roared past at speed. I stuck my thumb out half-heartedly. The driver stared serenely through me and didn't stop. I raised two fingers. The driver couldn't see but it made me feel a lot better.

What a lousy day, I muttered. My old man hadn't helped. I'd heard his load of bull a hundred times.

'I shouldn't ever have stood guarantor for you! You promised your mother you wouldn't do anything stupid on that death-trap of yours. So what happens? Police on the doorstep. Your mother back on valium. What were you thinking of? Sixty in a built-up area! *Sixty!*'

'Ah, shut up, Dad. We got enough troubles at 10.30 without you goin' on at me.' I mouthed the words again, spitting them out into the chilly drizzle, and kicked the kerb viciously. An elderly lady who'd been driving past slowly in a Metro glared at me and put her foot down. As she revved off in a cloud of spray I could almost hear Dad's angry retort all over again.

'Trouble? You don't know what trouble *is*, boy! It's me you'll be crawing to when they slap a hundred quid fine on you. I just hope they take your licence instead of my money.'

'Come off it, Dad.' I'd really been very cool indeed. 'I told you before, I pay my own debts. They'll give me time to pay. It ain't grand larceny, after all.'

'That's it, that's it! Make light of it! And what would've happened if you'd knocked somebody over?

Manslaughter, that'd be.'

'I'm not up for manslaughter, because I haven't run anybody over. I *have* been done for speeding. Which I might add, I've seen you do often enough in the Escort.'

Dad had ranted on like he always did. 'There's a difference between 35 miles an hour and 60, my boy'.

I didn't bother to remember the rest of the argument. I knew it all by heart. I was more bothered by the rain trickling down my collar at the back and the fact that the inside of my trouserlegs seemed to be as wet as the outside. I tried not to make sudden movements so the clammy cloth wouldn't touch my skin. The traffic was building up now. Nobody took any notice of me.

Things were looking grim. If somebody didn't stop soon I'd be done for not showing up at court. That would really give the old man something to rant about. He thought I was going by train in case they took my licence; but hitching didn't cost anything and I had a feeling I might soon be needing all the cash I could find.

I swore drearily. My breath disappeared into the drizzle, a tiny cloud. *Thank God Mum stayed in bed. I bet she took a load of Valium last night.* Valium always made Mum drowsy. She'd never stopped worrying since I collected the Honda. But if it hadn't been the bike it would have been something else to worry about. She was brilliant at worrying over things which never actually happened. *She got it right this time,* I scowled. *Bless her cotton socks.*

My own socks were soggy where the rain had got into my shoes. I was beginning to wonder how I would dry out if I ever got to court. I didn't fancy dripping all over the dock so some magistrate could make sarcastic comments.

8

My thoughts drifted to Louise. They often did.

'You'll lose that girl,' Mum had warned me last night when Louise had rung off. 'That's a nice girl, that is. Is she going to stand by you?'

I laid my hand on my heart and generally hammed it up. 'Yes, Mother — I believe she will. However long it takes. I may be bald, fat and forty by the time they let me out — but she'll wait, and there'll always be a candle burning in her window for my return.' I grinned. Mum hadn't smiled.

'You might be laughing now but you'll never find another as good as Louise.'

That was getting uncomfortably near the truth. I shook the idea out of my mind. I'd stopped sticking my thumb out by now and was just standing by the road-side getting wetter and wetter. Some drivers looked at me curiously, and occasionally passengers saw me and pointed me out to their friends. Nobody stopped.

Louise wasn't a nagger, though she'd never liked the bike. She was religious, just like Mum, but she seemed to get more out of it than Mum did. They both went to the same church, but I guarantee they had different ideas about who God was supposed to be. Louise used to just say quietly 'Tom, I'm praying for you' — and I'd feel stronger and safer, on my bike, at work, wherever — because she'd said that.

Cool, calm Louise. Just thinking about her unwound the knots of anger in my stomach.

Beep-beep!

I hadn't noticed the expensive blue Peugeot pulling up a hundred yards down the road. I ran up to it and peered through the window.

'Where are you going?' asked the driver.

'Oxford.'

'Hop in.'

The door closed with a gentle thud and I sank back into the plush seat. The driver glanced at me. It was a searching glance.

'I'd put your belt on if I were you.'

I stretched my legs out and relaxed. 'Never wear the things. Too restricting,' I volunteered. I was the tough type. I didn't even wear a crash helmet on the bike.

The driver merely repeated his suggestion. He looked about seventy years old. He didn't have to impress anybody any more. He had a quiet sort of authority in his voice. I slid the buckle into its clasp. A smile flickered briefly across his face, as if he was pleased with his minor triumph.

I stared ahead. The wipers were lurching back and forth across the windscreen, clearing water in sheets. The road appeared intermittently through the rain.

'Student?'

'Nope.'

'Off to work?'

'Nope.'

I knew I sounded arrogant, and after all, the guy had let me drip all over his upholstery; but I hadn't expected a cross-examination. What would the old boy do if I told him the truth? I decided to play a little game.

'If you must know,' I sighed, 'I'm off to court.' As soon as I'd said it I wished I hadn't.

'I'm sorry,' he said. The genuine concern in his voice surprised me. We fell silent. I was the first to speak.

'Don't you want to know what for?' I asked, half-menacingly. The old man shook his head.

'No — not unless you want to tell me. After all, I haven't told you where I'm going.'

I was disarmed. 'I'm only facing a speeding charge,' I

blurted. 'I got done for going through a village late at night. Can you believe it? There wasn't anyone else on the road. The Smokey must have been waiting to catch somebody just for the fun of it. I suppose he gets a day off to go to court.' I turned to him. 'I suppose you're like the rest of 'em. Nobody likes bikers.'

'Nobody?' he queried mildly. 'It might interest you to know that I was once the proud owner of a BSA.'

His moustache twitched as if at a pleasurable memory.

'*You?*' I was wide-eyed.

He guffawed. 'We're not born like this, you know!' He smoothed his white hair. 'I could have whipped you when I was half my years.'

I was stung by his assurance.

'Did you ever speed?' I demanded. 'I mean, were bikes *able* to in those days?'

He was unconcerned at my sarcasm. 'When I was your age I couldn't even afford a push bike. When the war ended I was thirty-six, and I thought "Bert, if you don't get mobile now, you never will." I went for BSA because I'd ridden them in the war. You might not believe it, but even with all your modern technology those old bikes would still give you a good run for your money.'

His eyes lit up when he talked about bikes. This guy was all right. He was a biker.

'How fast were you going when they caught you?' It was as if he was comparing notes.

'Sixty-two.'

'In thirty?'

'Yeah.'

He glanced involuntarily at the speedometer and rear-view mirror. 'I was once stopped for forty-five,' he remarked. 'But they let me off without a ticket.'

By now I would have believed anything of this unusual pensioner, who had the quiet authority that I'd noticed seemed to go with success. I wasn't turned off by it, either. He seemed genuine and direct, and I responded to him. I was curious to know more about him. 'What do you do for a living?' I asked.

'I was in timber exports for years. But that was only what I did for bread-and-butter. What I did for a *living* was much more exciting.' He paused. I asked him what he meant.

'I was — still am — a Methodist lay preacher.'

I laughed. I thought he was joking. 'Not much life in that, surely?'

He turned his head and looked at me penetratingly. 'Now hold on. You were complaining that everyone is against bikers. Have you ever considered — most people are against biking because they've never tried it? You don't like it when people are prejudiced against you. How about giving me a break?'

I nodded, 'Right. Fair enough.'

'Do you ever go to church?' he demanded abruptly.

I went onto the defensive at once. 'My Mum does, and my girlfriend. She even phoned last night to say she'd be praying for me today — how about that?'

'D'you ever discuss church with her?'

'Are you kidding! She's for ever trying to convert me. Mum says nothing. She gave up ages ago. But Louise — she takes it seriously. She's given me books to read and she's always trying to explain it to me.' I shifted in my seat and toyed with the seams of my still-damp trouser-legs. 'To be honest, it's all confusing. My Dad says the church is full of hypocrites. But he's probably the biggest hypocrite there is, with my Mum a close second.'

I stopped speaking and waited to be told off; that

wasn't the way to talk to a preacher. But his answer took me aback.

'Your Dad's partly right, I'm afraid. The church has its fair share of hypocrites. Have you ever seen a counterfeit penny?'

I frowned. 'No.'

'Quite. There wouldn't be any point, would there? If you're going to forge money you forge fivers or ten pound notes. Who'd bother to forge pennies?'

'Yes,' I admitted. 'But I don't see . . .'

'That's what's happened to Christianity,' he continued calmly. 'People see its value, especially where it deals with morals; and they try to copy it instead of getting hold of the real thing. The sad part of it is that it's easier to be a real Christian than a phony one.'

'My Louise's real,' I told him firmly. 'Do you know, she wouldn't marry me? She said we hadn't got the most important thing of all in common. Can you credit it? I know I'm out of work but it's not my fault; they made me redundant. I start a new job next week — really good prospects. I'd even have given up the bike and bought a car, but no, that flamin' Christianity comes right between us.'

I snorted angrily and clenched my fists, glaring ahead. The rain had practically gone. Only a few drops spattered uncertainly on the windscreen. My companion leaned forward and switched off the wipers. 'It might bring you together one of these days,' he said thoughtfully.

I burst out, 'The night I proposed she tried to tell me how to become a Christian myself. Me — Tom Woodhouse — a Christian! I told her, I'm as good a man as the next. Bit of a wild one on the bike, maybe; I like a drink or two like anyone else. But I wouldn't go out of my way to harm anybody.'

I finished. He negotiated another roundabout, sliding through the gears expertly. 'Is that what you think it's all about, Tom? Is it just a matter of being as good as the next bloke?'

'Well it is, isn't it? The whole point's doing what you're told. Obeying the commandments, innit? That's why Louise is so good. She says she's no better than me, but I know she is. She's the number one candidate for "up there".'

'Up where?'

'Heaven, of course.'

'Are you going to be there too?'

The question was casually put. I answered warily. 'You must be joking. I'm the one who's going to court, remember?'

'Would you like to go there?'

'Heaven? No. I'm more interested in what's happening now, today. I'm not thinking of dying just yet.'

There was another lull in the conversation. My clothes were dry now, and I was enjoying the warmth of the car. I watched the world go by and sank further back into the comfortable seat.

'JOBS NOT BOMBS'

Someone had sprayed the slogan in black paint on the white cement of the bridge we were just passing under. 'I suppose your boss wrote that,' I quipped. 'Hope it works. Otherwise we'll all be dead.'

'Oh! So you're afraid of dying!' He smiled. 'Would you like to know what the Bible has to say on the subject? It says that it's possible to know for certain that if you were to die today, you would go to heaven.'

I considered cautiously. After all, I wasn't all that sure I wanted to go there anyway.

14

'Want to hear more?' asked my companion.

I shrugged. 'Sure. Can't do any harm.'

I had an idea I was letting myself in for something. On the other hand, I wasn't too worried. The man was old enough to be my father, but he was interesting and sincere. I even began to feel excited. I'd never heard anyone speak about Christianity before the way he did. His moustache twitched when he talked about the Bible the same way it had when he'd spoken of his BSA bike. Maybe he had got something worth listening to. I decided to give him a hearing.

2
The Old Man tells it straight

'OXFORD: 10 MILES' . . . As we cruised past the sign, the old man settled back comfortably in his seat. *Ten miles to go,* I thought. *He'll have to talk fast if he's going to say anything worth hearing.*

'Odd, you know,' he began. 'Hardly anybody gives any thought to the business of dying. Mind you, when people get to my age it begins to be a bit more important to them . . . but at your age, who cares?'

I nodded. He looked at me shrewdly.

'I didn't think about it much either,' he remarked. 'But . . .' he added seriously, 'when I *did* think about it, it frightened the wits out of me.'

I stared ahead. I wasn't saying anything.

'I used to ask myself all sorts of questions I couldn't answer,' he continued. 'You know the sort of thing. "Why are we here?" — "Where are we going?" — "Where am *I* going?" I forgot all about such notions for most of the time. but every now and then I found myself thinking: maybe this world isn't all there is. Maybe there's something else. And that's what frightened me.'

I nodded agreement involuntarily, and jerked my head up hoping he hadn't noticed. He carried on. 'It wasn't until I'd been a Christian for a long time that I realised how important it is to be *certain* about eternal life — the hereafter — whatever you want to call it. I mean, I found it was important, not for later on but for here and now! And now that I know, I've got confidence to face anything life can throw at me.'

The traffic had slowed. We were approaching a roundabout. The old man switched gears and turned to look at me quizzically. 'Bet you think I'm really arrogant — eh? Well, I know I'm going to heaven and I can't help it if that sounds conceited!' He changed back into top and the car resumed its smooth progress. 'But you know, Tom,' he added thoughtfully, 'it's just because I know I'm going to heaven that I realise how tiny and insignificant I actually am.'

I wriggled on my seat. This was all sounding a bit too religious.

'A moment ago,' the old man said, 'you said that Louise was going to heaven — because she is a good person.'

I nodded aggressively. 'Right. She is.'

'But Tom, do you know *why* she insists she's no better than you?'

'No idea.'

'I can tell you.' The old man smiled. 'Louise knows heaven is a gift from God that she doesn't deserve. Nobody deserves to go to heaven. It's a gift.'

'Come off it,' I snorted. 'That would mean anybody could go.'

'That's how it is, Tom.' He recited some words softly. I recognised them. They were from the Bible. I'd heard Louise say them. '"By grace you have been saved through faith . . . and this not from yourselves; it is the gift of God — not from works, so that no-one can boast."'

'You're a lay-preacher,' I retorted. 'That's your book. You believe the Bible. I don't.' I wondered whether I should pull my punches. No; I had to have my say. 'You see — I just think of it as just like any other book. It's simply not that special.' I waited for his reply. I'd really found a crushing answer. Maybe I'd been a bit cruel. I felt guilty.

The old man wasn't bothered at all. 'You can believe the Bible or not as you please, Tom. That's your right and you're entitled to it. But really — *just* like any other book? Are you sure you mean that? How can a book that has been translated into more languages than any other, that has survived two or three thousand years, that has been read by more people and changed more lives than any other book — how can it be "just like any other book"?'

'Well, no, that's not what I meant, of course it isn't.' I was back-pedalling and I knew it. 'I mean it's like a good history book — like writings from ancient times — but it's important, sure, I can see that.'

My driver kept his eyes on the road and didn't rub the point home too hard. 'Well, a great many people would say, Tom, that it's the word of God. A book God uses to speak to mankind about the really important things. You know what it says? "These things are written so that you may have eternal life." What kind of things does it say on that subject? Any ideas?'

I went scarlet. The wily old bat was gently reminding me that I was rubbishing something I hadn't even read. He smiled, a friendly smile without gloating. 'Well, it tells us that heaven is a free gift, as I said before. We didn't earn it and we don't deserve it. In fact, if we had to earn the right to heaven half of us would lose out because we hadn't been brought up properly — or put it another way: if you had to be good to get into heaven, how good do you think you would have to be?'

I knew the answer to that one. 'As good as Louise, for starters.'

He shook his head gravely. 'Not good enough, Tom. God's standard is — absolute perfection. If you're not absolutely perfect, you've failed outright.'

The unfairness of it shook me. I spat the words out. 'Then no-one can go. No-one's perfect. Stands to reason.' I swivelled round and glared at him. 'If it comes to that — you aren't perfect either!'

I subsided, embarrassed. I started to mumble some sort of an apology. He shook his head. 'But you're right, Tom. Right first time. You just said exactly what the Bible says. No, I mean it. We're all in the same boat, Tom. "All have sinned." That's what the Bible says.'

'Sin!' I repeated. 'There you go again. You're using Louise's words. She keeps saying I'm a "sinner". I thought a sinner was someone who went to prison.' At that moment another road sign welcomed us to Oxford. I suddenly remembered where I was going. 'After today — I might be!' I laughed. He grinned. He was a sport, at least.

'I'll drive you down to the court. I'm not in any great hurry.'

'Thanks,' I muttered, half-unwilling to continue this conversation. We were passing between grey-walled college buildings, threading our way between rows of parked cars. Cyclists wavered in front of us. He slowed down to pass one, and kept his speed down afterwards. I knew why. He wanted to be sure he had time to finish.

'Sin . . . How best to explain it? You can certainly say that it's the attitude towards God that makes us do stupid and harmful things. He's God, and so he has authority over our lives. But we don't like being told what to do. None of us do. We prefer to do things our way. Right?'

'Right!' I was in full agreement there.

'And that sets up a chain reaction — like pushing the first domino in the row over — down they flip, one by one — first we rebel against God, then we set ourselves up as number one. And that's how things start to go wrong. Like your little problem today.'

I shrugged in bravado. Took more than a court case to throw *me*.

'Certain roads have speed limits. Actually they're set up for everybody's safety. But from your point of view they're a limitation. You want to drive as fast as you like. But when you're caught you've no defence. You can't plead that you wanted to go faster than the legal limit. You certainly can't argue that everyone else is doing it anyway. That will only make the magistrate more determined to take one offender at least off the road — you.'

'Yeah, but I was only telling my Dad this morning — it's no use him going on at me when he drives over the limit himself — *and* on his way back from the pub.'

'But that isn't the point, is it?' he said calmly. I fell silent. There wasn't much to say. He continued softly.

'We're all sinners, Tom. We can't do anything about it ourselves. You broke just one law — quite a small one, really. But here you are going to court for it. And it's just the same between us and God. The Bible says that if we keep the whole of God's laws and miss just one, it's as bad as if we'd broken every single one. The only thing we can do is to trust God's mercy. And you know, Tom, he is merciful. He loves us. He doesn't want to punish us.'

He brought the car to a halt. 'Here we are. Oxford Magistrate's Court. And I'd hardly begun talking! When will you be finished in here?'

I jerked my thoughts back to the business in hand. Why had he stopped just as it was getting interesting? 'Oh — I should think it'll be an all-day stint,' I muttered.

He smiled. 'Tell you what, old son. I'll come back when my business is finished, find you, and we'll have a bite to eat together. Then I can have the pleasure of your company on the way home.'

I couldn't believe my luck. This lousy day was turning out OK after all. Maybe Louise had been praying like she'd promised — her prayers had a habit of working out!

'I'll park my car at the bottom of the steps. OK?' He gripped my hand and shook it. 'Good luck in court, Tom.' He smiled at me gravely as I got out of the car.

'See you later,' I said nervously. I turned my collar up against the cold. He started up the car. I went into the courthouse.

3
Court-room drama

I checked my digital. 10.15 — I wasn't late. I pushed open the heavy door and went into a small waiting room that smelled of polish and stale cigarettes. Most of the seats were occupied; couples and small groups, each separated from the rest by one empty chair. *Blow that, for a start,* I muttered to myself.

Facing me were two more imposing doors, thick panelled jobs with loads of carving and brass handles. They were numbered: 1 and 2. I wondered which one I'd be going through.

Several of the others were staring at me curiously. I looked back brazenly, but could feel myself going red in the face. I saw a door with a sign labelled 'Men', and thankfully retreated to the gents where a beetroot-faced Tom Woodhouse gazed back at me from a bevelled mirror. I made my way to the cubicles. I needed to sit down.

Perched on the loo I gathered my thoughts together. The old man had distracted me from my worries on the way up to Oxford. But now I had to think about my defence. Defence? The solicitor had already told me, I hadn't got one. I would just have to plead guilty and hope they'd decide there were mitigating circumstances.

Please, your honour, I fantasised, *I plead guilty but hope that you'll understand that when faced with the temptation of the open road I just had to give in and burn up the tarmac . . .*

Oh, that's quite all right, Mr. Woodhouse, consider yourself mitigated. Please collect your expenses from the clerk.

May we apologise on behalf of the Thames Valley Fuzz what simply do not understand that young people have to try out their wings . . .

There was a noise of the adjoining loo being flushed. I reluctantly abandoned my daydream and went back to the waiting room. A black-gowned man was calling a register. It was like being back at school. I grunted when my name was called and tried to look as inconspicuous as possible. There were a pile of magazines on a table. I picked them up and put them down again. *Time, Country Life, The Lady* . . . they seemed to get a high class of criminal in these courts.

Another gowned official was pinning up several pieces of paper. I joined the crush of people trying to read them. My name was among the rest — No. 41: Thomas James Woodhouse of 22 Cirencester Rd. Southampton. At least it was inconspicuous among all the other bits and pieces of magistrates' business that filled the paper. 'Excess speed. £200. Lic. end. Disq. opt . . . Application for occasional licence . . . No insurance . . . Excess alcohol . . . Defective headlamp . . . Failure to provide a breath specimen . . . Failure to produce a driving licence . . . No test certificate . . .'

I looked at the list. *It must be awfully difficult to stay out of court these days,* I thought. The people around were still pushing. An American airman was looking at his own charges and demanding, 'What's a Lic. end.?'

'Licence endorsed!' chorused a number of knowledgeable English voices. The airman peered again at the list. 'And Disq. opt.?'

'That means they're planning on disqualifying you — you'd better get your kite out!' replied a cockney wit, breathing on the airman's shoulder brass and pretending to polish it with his sleeve. The airman laughed with the rest of us and moved away.

'Woodhouse? Thomas Woodhouse?'

My solicitor was looking for me. He was a weedy-looking guy in a creased suit. He looked flustered.

'I'm here,' I whispered, half-hoping no-one had noticed me.

'I just want to go through the drill with you before we go in. Follow me, will you?' We made our way through the door marked '2' into an almost empty court room. More panelled wood but no stale cigarette smoke this time. Three policemen were whispering together in one corner; a youngish man was seated in front of the Bench. It was just like the telly. Nobody acknowledged our presence. 'You will stand here while the charge is being read. Then sit down. I shall not be calling you to the stand as I shall be making a statement of the facts on your behalf after the prosecuting police officer has given his side of the story. OK?' He rattled through the information. It was all old hat to him. I nodded. I was a new boy. It sounded OK to me. Afterwards, we went back to the waiting room.

The morning wore on. I heard the clock over my head ticking. People left to go into the court room. I was last to be called. As we went in I passed the American airman. He was pale, almost tearful, and he was counting five-pound notes off a roll into the clerk's hands. *At least he's got the cash*, I thought enviously, as I entered the court room, now full of people. I took up my position where I had been told. My mouth was dry and my insides were doing funny things. Had the solicitor told me to sit or stand? I couldn't remember. I stood. Nobody seemed in any hurry to start. I looked at the three figures on the bench.

The woman on the left was a tweedy, aggressive-looking, threatening individual.

The woman on the right looked about thirty; timid,

small — the sort who'd let you off if she could.

The man in the centre was elderly, with a small moustache, and I had last seen him driving a blue Peugeot.

He gave no sign of recognition. I avoided his eyes and looked instead at the unicorn crest hung over his head on the wall. My mind was racing with shock and a lot of anger.

'Do you understand the charge?'

I hadn't even heard it read out. I muttered something which the clerk assumed was agreement.

'Do you wish to plead guilty or not guilty?'

'Guilty,' I choked.

I was told to sit down. My face must have reflected the sick feeling that was all I had inside me now, because some people sitting nearby looked at me in concern. The old man spoke from the bench. 'Are you feeling unwell, Mr. Woodhouse?'

'No, Sir,' I lied.

A police officer gave evidence of my misdemeanor, digging my grave effectively and calmly. The solicitor finished the job off. 'This young man wishes to express his deep regret that he has ridden his motor cycle at such speed and with such noise through the peaceful village of Ashley at night. He wishes to state that he will never do this again . . .' As he droned on with his pathetic appeal, I watched the magistrates out of the corner of my eye. I began to think differently about things. I might have hit really lucky. Hadn't the old boy picked me up? That meant he was a sympathetic type to start with . . . and didn't he actually admit that he'd speeded on a BSA? And got off?

The old man was listening intently to the appeal, his head on one side, resting on clasped hands. *Conditional*

Discharge, I thought. *That's it, it's bound to be that. The old rogue knew I was up before him. Didn't he offer me a lift back? Anyway, what's a bloke from Hampshire doing in an Oxford court room?*

'We shall retire to consider our verdict,' said my chauffeur of that morning. He gave an almost knowing glance in my direction as the three of them went out. I watched the police and the clerk of the court laughing together as they waited. *Boy, are they in for a shock*, I gloated, now anxious to see the door open and hear the verdict.

They came back. I was told to stand up. The old man gave a dry cough and began.

'You have pleaded guilty to the charge.' He was looking me straight in the eyes. No sign of recognition. What a character he was turning out to be! 'You are very fortunate in my opinion not to be here on a charge of dangerous driving. 62 miles an hour — even at 11.30 at night — is dangerous. We have discussed disqualifying you from driving. It is however my opinion that you need a lesson which disqualification will not provide. Fined one hundred and fifty pounds.'

No! That's wrong! You're supposed to let me off — Conditional Discharge —

I wanted to scream it out; my fists clenched, my knuckles went white. The swine — he knew this was the end of my bike. Bang went my hire purchase payments. How do you find a hundred and fifty quid on the dole? Suddenly he wasn't a kind old man any more. I hated him.

The clerk was doing his clerk thing. 'How do you want to pay?'

'I'll need time . . .' I snarled. I knew I'd have to sell my Honda.

There was a conference on the bench. The women

nodded. The old man addressed me again. His moustache was twitching. The lust for blood, I supposed.

'You will meet me in ten minutes outside the office to the left of the waiting area. Do you understand?'

'Yes Sir.' I dragged the 'Sir' out reluctantly.

'The court will stand . . .'

'What's going on?' I demanded of the solicitor, as people began to file out of the court room after the magistrates' departure. He shrugged and looked blank. 'I don't know — this is a new one on me. You'd better do as he says.'

We weren't kept waiting the full ten minutes. My one-time friend appeared in his overcoat. *A good morning's work over*, I scowled. He looked slightly embarrassed; both hands stuck deep in his pockets and his shoulders hunched in a contrived casual pose. As our eyes met he flushed.

'Your licence will be sent to Swansea for endorsement. It will be returned in two or three weeks.' He paused. Then he pulled a piece of paper from his pocket and thrust it at me. 'Here. You'll want to keep this.' He nodded to the solicitor and made for the exit. I watched him go, uncomprehending.

'Let's have a look,' said the solicitor, and took the paper. His brow creased.

'Paid? Paid? How can it be paid?'

He sprang into the clerk's office. After a minute or so I heard him bellowing. 'You have to be joking! He paid the fine? I never heard anything like it in all my days!'

He reappeared. 'Well, you lucky young beggar, it seems you didn't need me here today after all. Your fine's been paid. I just don't understand. If he wanted to let you off, why not give you a Conditional Discharge? But to slap a hefty fine on you and then pay it himself . . . I don't get it, I really don't.'

He shook my hand, gave me the paper, and walked off leaving me on my own.

I was still clutching the receipt for one hundred and fifty pounds as I left the building and stood on the pavement. The November chill and the dampness after the rain made me shiver as I pulled my collar up and began to think about going home.

Beep! Beep!

I turned and saw the gleaming blue Peugeot parked nearby, a shock of white hair visible through the driver's window.

'Coming, Tom?' called the strong voice, above the purring of the engine and the noises of the city.

I moved towards the car. The passenger door opened invitingly. Once again I sat back in the plush seat, and reached for my safety belt. I shook my head in bewilderment. This was a strange geezer, and no mistake.

4
Homeward bound

'Why did you pay my fine?'

My question broke a silence which had lasted for several minutes after we had left the courthouse. The old man thought for a moment before he answered. 'To teach you a lesson.'

'What lesson?' I demanded.

The old man raised his eyebrows. 'You tell me.'

'Well,' I countered argumentatively, 'so far it's taught me I can speed on my bike and be let off.'

'Were you let off?'

'Course I was. You paid the fine.'

'And a fine is a penalty?'

'Right.'

'Then you weren't let off.'

There was another interval while I digested the argument. I could see his point. I tried again. 'Well, you know what I mean.'

'I do,' he replied. 'But do you know what I mean?'

I fixed my gaze on the tax disc in front of me, and worked out what I was going to say next. 'No I don't get you at all. Why didn't you give me a Conditional Discharge, if you wanted to let me off? That's what I was hoping you'd do. And you'd have saved yourself a hundred and fifty quid.'

The old man laughed. 'Tell me, Tom, how long d'you reckon you can sit there without saying anything?'

I coloured up. 'I dunno — what do you mean?'

'Well, I need you to stay quiet long enough for me to

explain myself. Think you can manage that? I'll try to be as concise as I can.'

I shrugged. After all, I was feeling pretty grateful to the old guy. And anyway I wanted to find out how his mind was working. 'OK. Go on.'

He made himself comfortable, adjusted his rear-view mirror, flicked a speck of dirt off his sleeve, stroked his moustache, and began to speak.

'On our way to court this morning, I was trying — not very successfully, I'm afraid — to explain the basic message of the Bible to you; that is, how you can know for certain that you have eternal life. You remember we talked about the fact that it's not just to do with being good enough for God. His standard is absolute perfection — remember? We've all done wrong. Even your friend Louise.'

'OK.' I was getting quite interested again. And whatever all this Bible stuff was, it certainly seemed to be very important to the old man. You could tell that by the way he talked.

'Right, Tom. Well, the Bible tells us two things about God that stand out above everything else. First: he loves us and doesn't want to punish us.'

I nodded. That was OK by me.

'Second — he is absolutely just, and because of that he has to punish sin. That's what justice means. In fact he's already passed the sentence. It says so in the Bible. "The wages of sin is death." So we have a contradiction. He loves us and doesn't want to punish us; on the other hand he hates sin and his justice demands we be punished.'

Light was beginning to dawn. 'So this morning . . .'

'Yes. It was a bit like that. And if God simply let us off he'd be no more just than I would have been if I'd let *you* off. You were guilty and there was a penalty for your offence.'

'I see,' I said thoughtfully.

The old man's voice had an edge of urgency. 'Tom: I didn't want to teach you merely the foolishness of speeding. I wanted to show you, practically, how mercy and justice can operate simultaneously. I paid your fine; what the law demanded was paid, in full, finished. But at the same time I was able to show love towards you, because I paid the fine you should have paid. The one doesn't contradict the other . . . And that's what God did for you, Tom.'

'How do you mean?' I wasn't being sarcastic. I really wanted to know.

'He came to this earth as Jesus Christ to pay your fine — to die — for you. He was the only perfect man who ever lived — but because of you and me, he died like a common criminal. You know how the Bible puts it? "He has reconciled you by Christ's physical body through death, to present you holy in his sight, without blemish, and free from accusation" . . . You've got that receipt in your pocket. Nobody can touch you for that speeding offence ever again. You can smile now when you see a policeman. The Bible's like that, Tom. It's God's receipt to you. It says that your penalty for your sins has been fully paid. Christ died instead of us. He rose from death — that proves the sort of power he has — and went to heaven; and now he offers us the gift of eternal life. And we get it by faith — by believing.'

He paused. 'Does all that make sense to you?'

'Yes,' I replied thoughtfully. 'It's what Louise keeps telling me. But I never understood it before. Never really listened, in fact.'

We were on the open road now, and trees and fields were flashing by. I racked my brains for something to say. On an impulse I asked him, 'How come you live in Southampton and you're an Oxford magistrate?'

He laughed. 'I've a cottage in Cadnam I use as a retreat. I'm semi-retired now. I still have ties with Oxford — mainly church and JP work.'

'Bit of a fluke you saw me this morning,' I volunteered.

'Could be,' he replied. 'Or perhaps part of God's plan. Maybe he wanted me to speak to you today.'

I contemplated the possibility. I'd never thought of such a thing until that moment.

It was me that brought the conversation back to the subject of God. I can't remember whether I wanted to or not — I know I was feeling really mixed up inside. But I knew one thing. If I was going to talk about the Bible with somebody, it was going to be with him. He didn't know me from Adam, he seemed really concerned for me, and he acted like no other old person I'd ever come across.

So I dropped my tough image and talked with him straight.

'What do you have to *do*?' I asked him. 'I mean, if someone wants to be a Christian? Don't jump to any conclusions, now —' (I really didn't want him to, it wasn't sarcasm) '— I understand what you're saying, but I'm not going to turn Christian just because you paid my fine for me. I couldn't live with that.'

He was unperturbed. 'Good! Neither could I!' he smiled. Then his face became serious. 'You say you understand. But do you *believe* in what we've been talking about? And more than that — if you believe in it, do you agree with it? Are you going to do anything about it?'

There was a tight, excited feeling in the pit of my stomach. I really did believe it. The whole lot. It made sense. He'd explained it so I didn't have any more questions — not big ones, anyway. Whether Noah's ark was true and whether astronauts had visited the earth and what ghosts were about and all that — that could wait. But I was sure about what God had done. It was a crazy feeling. I looked at the old man.

'Sure I believe. But I dunno that I could do anything about it. Not yet.'

His eyes were bright. 'That's good, Tom! That's wonderful! You believe — praise the Lord!'

Last time I heard somebody say that was in a TV comedy. It sounded different, coming from him.

'But you know,' he added, 'faith — that's what the Bible says salvation is all about — starts with belief, but you have to go on to *trust* what you believe in.'

He tapped the steering wheel gently with the fingers of one hand. 'Put your trust, Tom, in what Jesus has done for you. Repent of your sin.'

'I don't know what that means,' I muttered. But I had a good idea what it did . . .

He frowned, thinking hard. 'Let me ask you a question, Tom. Are you ever going to break the speed limit again?'

I wasn't sure what he wanted me to say so I told the truth. 'I don't know. I hope not. Wouldn't show much gratitude, would it? I'll try to stay the right side of the limit. Honestly, I will.'

'You mean — partly because it's the law, and partly because of what I did? That it?'

'Right.'

'That's repentance,' he exclaimed. 'It's making a U-turn in the way you think. Like suddenly seeing a road-sign that says you're thirty miles in the opposite direction from where you wanted to be going — what would that mean?'

'It'd mean I'd got on the wrong road.'

'That's right! And I can be as sorry as I like about it, and make as many apologies as I like, and believe I'm on the wrong road — even *know* I'm on the wrong road; but as long as I keep driving, I'm getting further and further away from where I want to be. So what should I do?'

'Turn round,' I said quietly, 'and get on the right road.'

We talked a lot after that, but I knew I'd answered my own question. The gospel, he said, was the signpost that said I'd been going in the wrong direction. All I had to do was make a U-turn. Plead guilty to God and accept him paying my penalty. Just like I'd taken the old man's receipt. Trust him as my Saviour, as the old man put it; make him Lord of my life, where he belonged.

We were still talking when we reached Southampton. As I unbuckled the safety belt he gave me his card. 'Give me a call if I can be of any more help.'

'You bet,' I said. 'And — thanks.'

He reached over and shook my hand. He had a warm, strong grip.

It's not every day a judge pays your fine, I said to myself as his car purred away. Whatever would Louise say? I scratched my head, stood thinking for a moment, and made for home.

5
A rum reception

I turned the key in the front door lock as quietly as I could. I knew my mum would be full of questions. Probably worried sick that I'd been sent to jail or worse.

Ever so gently, I pushed the door open and made my entrance into the familiar clutter. I took a deep breath and braced myself for the grand entrance. 'I'm home,' I called.

There was silence. I tried again. 'I'm back!'

All remained quiet.

I poked my head into the sitting room on my way to the kitchen. Surely Mum would come bustling through any minute? I looked through the window into the garden. No sight or sound of anybody. Upstairs; into the bedroom; nobody. The house was empty. Not a soul to tell my good news to.

I flopped onto my bed, clasped my hands behind my head, and reviewed the day.

What on earth would Mum and Dad say? Who ever heard of a magistrate paying a fine? And Louise? I gazed at the snapshot on my bedside table, the two of us on the beach at Swanage in the summer. That was the day on which I'd proposed. What a fool I'd felt, tossing stones at an empty ice-cream wrapper, trying to look as cool as James Bond.

'How about us to staying together then, Lou? I mean — you know — ug, I don't mean just shacking up together. I mean the whole works. Bells. Wedding rings and all that.'

When I remembered how she'd said 'No', a wave of

emotion swept over me. My fist thumped into the duvet. Then I reached for the photograph and held it high in front of me. 'Louise Dobson — whether you like it or not, we're going to get married!'

The photo smiled back at me, radiantly, untroubled. I scowled back. 'I'm blowed if I'm going to become a Christian just to please you,' I vowed. 'I know what you been up to. Talking to your Governor, right? "Please, God, make him believe" — well, you pulled a biggie out of the hat today. You really hit the jackpot. If I don't believe after that, I never will. . . .'

I realised what I'd said. I really did believe what the old man had been saying. Not that I could remember all that much of it; but for the first time, the whole idea of God, the Bible and the rest seemed perfectly credible.

I closed my eyes; yawned; and fell asleep.

An hour later I woke up suddenly to the noise of a familiar engine idling below my window and car doors being slammed. The quiet of the house was broken with bangs and clatters as the front door was opened and the garage doors slammed shut.

'Tom! Tom! Are you there?'

'Coming,' I shouted, and reluctantly rolled over and got to my feet. I was halfway down the stairs when Dad walked in through the front door. He saw me. I saw from his face that he was anxious. 'What happened, son?' he asked. 'How did you get on?'

'Well, it's difficult to say, actually . . .'

I saw Mum standing behind him, looking tense and worried as well. I continued, looking at her: 'In a way I got off. But in another — I didn't.'

'What do you mean?' my mother demanded. There was a weepy edge to her voice. I smiled reassuringly.

'Well, if you put the kettle on, I'll tell you both what

happened. But honestly, you won't believe it.' I put my arm round Mum and ushered her into the kitchen. She was really worried. I ended up making the tea myself as Mum and Dad got their coats off, sat down, and waited to hear my news.

'I was fined a hundred and fifty quid,' I began, calm and matter-of-fact. Dad's rection was as quick as it was predictable. 'Told you so! Told you so! Well, it's no use coming to me. I haven't got that sort of money to throw around, not just before Christmas. You're on your own, you hear me?' He wagged his finger at me; something I'd never seen him do before. 'Let this be a lesson to you! You might be an adult in the eyes of those berks at Westminster that dropped the voting age — but in my book you don't become an adult until you start acting like one. And you can start by paying your own debts.' He shook his head angrily. 'I knew this would happen. I knew it. Thank God it was Oxford and not here, or it'd have been all over the Echo as well.'

I felt really good. I watched the steam rise out of the kettle. Mum broke in, her voice taut.

'But you said you were let off.'

'I was.' I swivelled round to face them both and enjoyed the surprise I was about to give them. 'The judge paid my fine for me. Matter of fact, he gave me a lift back to Southampton as well.'

Mum looked blank. Dad just laughed humourlessly. 'OK, son. I get it. Now I'm listening. You got my full attention. So what really happened?'

I suddenly realised I'd have to tell him I'd been hitching. Some of the bounce went out of me. 'I kid you not, Dad. Here, I'll tell you about it.' And I told them the whole story, as their eyes grew wide and their faces registered disbelief. 'So you see, ' I finished, pouring the tea, 'I *was* let off — wasn't I?'

'Let off? Let off?' thundered Dad. 'I should say not! Who was that old man? He's not allowed to do that sort of thing. I'll bet he's a raving queer.'

'Fred!' squealed Mum.

'I'm telling you! Giving lifts to boys, indeed. Cheques for a hundred and fifty quid . . .'

'Come off it, Dad — I'm twenty, aren't I?'

'Oh, age don't make any difference, not to that sort. I'm telling you he's queer. How else d'you explain him picking you up out of the blue, paying your fine, driving you back, if you please — and then giving you his card and inviting you to go and see him any time?' He was really worked up now. 'You'd be better off sending a cheque to the court and telling them to send his back to him. In fact, I'll tell you what I'm going to do. I'll give you a cheque. I'll pay the ------ fine myself. And another thing' — he wheeled round and glared at me triumphantly — 'what's your little girl friend going to say about all this?'

'Hallelujah, if I know her,' I muttered, with a show of defiance. I sipped my tea and rattled my spoon in the saucer. *He'd change his tune*, I thought, *if he met the old guy*. 'You don't understand, Dad,' I protested as calmly as I could. 'The feller was trying to teach me a lesson I'd never forget,'

'Oh, yes! Sounds like it! What sort of a lesson does that carry-on teach you?'

So it was that I found myself explaining the message of Christianity to my church-going mother and my antagonistic father — all to excuse the kindness of an old man I'd just met. It was crazy. I did the best I could. My explanation was punctuated by guffaws from Dad and speechless incredulity from Mum. 'So you see,' I finished up uncertainly, 'he paid the fine to show me, you know — like an example? Of what Christ did

on the cross. It was a . . . what was the word he used? .
. . yeah, a parable. Uh — I remember. He said he did it
because it was like Jesus paying my penalty — wanting
to satisfy what the law wanted — and loving me at the
same time. That's what he said.'

'You flabber my ghast,' said Dad sourly. He wasn't a
man to open his mind to anything new. Mum, for her
part, was in tears. She couldn't speak.

'Now look what you've done,' said Dad. 'Come on,
Lil. Snap out of it. It's not worth upsetting yourself
over it. He's made his own bed and he'll have to lie on
it. God! I wish I'd given him more beltings before it was
too late.'

He stormed on, and Mum cried all the more, and I
stood between them wondering which of them to try to
relate to first.

The doorbell rang.

I escaped gratefully and went to the front door. I
could see Louise's unmistakable profile through the
smoked glass. *Thank goodness for that*, I breathed, and
swung the door open.

'Hi! How's the most wanted man in town?'

It was a couple of seconds before she became aware of
the tension.

'What's up?'

'Dad,' I mumbled. 'Up the flaming wall!'

She pecked me on the cheek and breezed into the
kitchen, treating both Mum and Dad to the same. They
relaxed visibly when she came in. Louise seemed to
create her own peace wherever she went. In no time, we
were actually talking about what had just happened.
Dad gave his own version of events, embroidering quite
a lot and paying not much attention to Mum's tears
which were still flowing. Louise poured herself a cup of

tea. I wondered, idly, whether it was still hot. Dad's prejudice and fury flowed over and past my ears. I waited for him to run out of steam. Eventually he subsided.

'You're a sensible girl, Louise. Now you just tell him.'

Louise smiled across at me. 'What does Tom say about all this?'

I gave my version again, even the religious bits.

Louise was oddly excited as I spoke. As I finished, she asked nervously, 'Did you make a decision?'

'A what?'

'A decision — about what the old man told you.'

I suddenly realised for her, the really important thing in all this was something that my parents seemed to have missed entirely. 'No, I didn't,' I shouted, and Louise's face fell. 'Can you imagine what it'd be like, being a Christian in this house? The archangel Gabriel couldn't live in a place this full of bigots. I thought you'd all be pleased! The old beak was only doing what he thought was right. He showed me more love in one morning than you've shown me in a lifetime. He explained more about Christianity than ten thousand flaming sermons — for once, I can really get hold of what it's all about — but what the hell's the point if your own parents suspect every move of someone they've never even met?'

I didn't wait for a reaction. I stormed upstairs, slammed the door of my room shut behind me, and buried my face in the pillow.

Some minutes passed by. A gentle knock on the door. Suddenly I felt wretched. Louise. Louise — in front of her, of all people. I heard the door open, but kept my face turned away. Then her gentle hands were stroking my hair. I was a turmoil inside. I couldn't face up to myself, let alone this girl I wanted to marry.

'You're wrong, Tom,' she whispered. 'They do love you. In a way, your father showed it by the way he got angry.'

I mumbled into my pillow. I wasn't going to see the truth of it.

'Your mother's been talking to me. She agrees with me, that the verdict and meeting the old man were both tremendous answers to our prayers. God must love you very much, Tom, to give you such an experience.'

Quiet fell between us. She rested her hand on my shoulder. 'Tom. Oh, Tom Woodhouse . . .' She paused. Then she said, hesitantly, 'Tom . . . why don't we pray about it?'

I turned round then, throwing the pillow aside. The suddenness of my movement almost threw her off the bed.

'*Me*?' I demanded. 'Come off it! I'm not the praying type, and you know it. What the heck should I have to pray about — except getting a pad of my own, a bit of independence, and be rid of all this?'

'There you go again, Tom. When are you going to stop running, and face the truth? I can't make the decision for you. Only you can do that. It's between you and God.'

It was like a dash of cold water in my face. I subsided. I decided I would give in to some of her pleas. But I wasn't praying with her. 'OK. We'll go and see the old boy together. I told him about you. You'll get on like a house on fire. You speak the same language.'

'OK,' she said. 'One condition. You go right now and apologise to your mum and dad.'

She was right. I went downstairs.

6
Hooked at Cadnum

Just another half-hour . . . I surrendered myself to the comforts of Sunday morning in bed. It was the weekly struggle of mind over mattress. Giving in compensated for the other mornings when, job-hunting, I rose at the unearthly hour of nine-thirty.

The half-hour I'd promised myself had another ten minutes to go when I was reawakened by the sound of a door being slammed shut below, and eight seconds later I heard the front gate crash against its post. Mum was off to church.

Why does she go? I wondered to myself. *It isn't that she really wants to be a hypocrite. She does her best. But it can't be easy with Dad always going on at her the way he does* . . .

I drowsily chased ideas round my mind, filling in the last few minutes before I got up. Then the telephone rang. Once. Twice. Three, four, five times. I grumbled as I threw back the duvet and made a dash for the stairs.

'76 2160,' I panted.

'Bet you've forgotten,' said Louise's voice.

'Forgotten what?'

'Told you so! We're going out to Cadnam to see Mr. Westbury — your judge friend — remember?'

'Course I remember,' I lied. 'I'll pick you up after lunch.'

Two hours later she was snuggling into my back as we rode on my Honda down the M27 towards the New Forest. I'd rung Mr. Westbury to tell him we were coming. He'd sounded quite enthusiastic.

His cottage stood among oaks and bracken, looking like a picture postcard as the pale sun filtered down through the trees. We looked at the front door, then at each other. Before we had summoned the courage to open the front gate we heard his voice behind us.

'Good! You're early!' He strode over to us out of the nearby trees. A dog was trotting alongside him, tongue lolling out of his mouth — they'd obviously been for a walk. The dog bounded up to us and wagged its tail furiously, barking loudly.

'Just taking Tammy for her afternoon run,' he explained, as he opened the gate and ushered us through. 'And this must be Louise.' He put a friendly arm round our shoulders and took us into the cottage. Minutes later we were sitting in front of an open log fire. His wife, a white-haired lady with an animated face, was spoiling us. She was like Louise, I decided almost at once; must be at least fifty years older, but like her in lots of ways. The same infectious enthusiasm and lack of stuffiness. I wondered whether Mr. Westbury had told her about his gift to me. How would she take it, I wondered? Would she be any different to my parents? Somehow, I suspected she would be.

I'm glad Louise is such a good talker, I reflected, sinking back into a large flower-patterned armchair. The three of them were talking nineteen-to-the-dozen, and the dog turned to me for attention with the doleful look of one knowing that it wasn't any use competing.

Mrs. Westbury passed me another cup of coffee. 'Tom,' she whispered, 'you have a fine woman here.' Her eyes twinkled. I liked her even more now. The idea of Louise being called a woman rather than a girl amused me at first — I would have thought a woman was somebody a lot older than me. But I had to let the thought go, as the three of them turned their attention to me. Louise was smiling and looking happy. I was glad she liked Mr. and Mrs. Westbury.

'So your father gave you a rough ride, Tom,' began the judge. 'I'm sorry to hear that. Perhaps I ought to write to him and explain. Eh? More important — what can I do for you?'

He leaned forward and attacked a smouldering log with the poker, sending a shower of sparks upwards.

I gave him a blow-by-blow account of events since he'd dropped me off in Southampton. I explained to him — in a way, it was like explaining to myself — that he'd made me see for the first time that Christianity wasn't just a matter of being a goody-goody and keeping your nose clean. 'But what I don't see is, if Jesus died to take the rap for me and has forgiven me, why do I need to do anything about it? Surely I can do what I like and still get to heaven at the end of it, if it's a free gift — can't I?'

'Well, Tom, let's go over what we talked about in the car, about what Jesus did; then we can go on to talk about what your reasons should be to that. OK?'

I listened eagerly as he once again explained very simply what he called the 'gospel'. He finished and looked me straight in the eye. 'Does that make sense, Tom?'

'Yes,' I replied honestly.

'Well then, Tom, it's like this. God does want you to do something about it. So long as you're being offered a gift, it's yours only in name. You *could* have it, but you haven't got it yet. It never will be yours — until you have actually received it. So the first thing God wants you to do is to make it yours. To put your trust in Jesus Christ, and ask him for the gift of eternal life. He wants you to repent of sin — remember, we talked about that?

He wants you to make a U-turn in your life, so that you are no longer living your own way just to please yourself, but are living God's way to please him. The Holy Spirit will help you to do this, and will bring you into a relationship with God and with God's people, the church.'

'That's my problem,' I said. 'I believe what you say about Christ, and I suppose if I'm honest with myself I want to repent as you call it and live for God' — Louise looked up, her eyes bright — 'but how the heck do I come to terms with the church? Louise and Mum go to the same church. Louise seems to get something real out of it. But Mum — she just goes out of habit. She's as neurotic as a hen with chicks. If I were to end up like that I'd have more problems with Christianity than without.'

I pressed on with my excuses, but inside I had to admit that I knew the difference between Louise and Mum. Louise had a faith that was alive. Poor Mum hadn't got the real thing. I knew which I needed.

Louise reached over and squeezed my hand. Mr. Westbury spoke quietly. 'Tom, do you feel you are ready to put your trust in Jesus Christ?'

It was a punch between the eyes; I hadn't finished arguing yet; but I found myself responding.

'Sure. I really want to.'

I looked at Louise. Her eyes were shining, and she was beaming.

And there, in front of that spitting log fire, I bowed my head and asked Jesus Christ to forgive my sins.

Mr. Westbury added his prayer to mine. 'Father, please take this young man and use him in any way you want. Make his life the instrument your love uses to reach others.'

As he finished, the impact of what I now believed hit me. God had loved me so much that he — the everlasting almighty God — had come to earth to die instead of me, because of the sins I had done. Why had it taken so long for such a simple truth to break through my thick skull? I, Tom Woodhouse, the cynic who had called himself an agnostic, had bowed my head before the love of God. Now I had a brand new life. I felt like shouting at the top of my voice, 'Wake up, world! Jesus loves you!'

7

Stained glass and wine

'I want you to have this. It's a present from the two of us,' said Mr. Westbury. 'It's a modern translation of the Bible — it will make it easier for you to understand what God wants to do with your life.' He wrote a few words on the flyleaf and handed it to me.

As I took the Bible, the roar of a motorcycle outside shattered the afternoon peace. I pricked up my ears as the deep revs pulsed and then died outside the cottage as the rider switched off his engine.

'That will be Paul.' A slight frown shadowed Mrs. Westbury's face as she rose and made her way to the heavy oak door. A few seconds later two leather-jacketed teenagers swaggered into the room, their heads ducking beneath the old beams. The taller of the two removed his black-visored helmet.

'Hi, Gramps!' he said cheerfully. 'Who's this?' He was looking at Louise. 'You should have said you'd got company. We'd have got here for lunch. This is Sebastian. Can you believe that? We call him Seb.'

The younger of the two, hovering uncertainly in the doorway, removed his helmet and smiled sheepishly at Mr. Westbury. His friend turned to me. 'Nice bike,' he acknowledged. 'Pity these Japs are so darned clever, isn't it? Still prefer my BMW.' He yawned, rubbed his hand across his red nose, and slumped into the only remaining chair, leaving Mrs. Westbury to sit on the arm of her husband's.

We were introduced. 'My grandson, Paul,' said the

judge. Paul waved a lazy hand in our direction. I got up, clutching my new Bible. 'We'll have to be moving along, Mr. and Mrs. Westbury. Thanks for all your help. We'll be in touch.'

Paul leaned out of his chair and peered at my Bible. 'What's that you've got?' He recognised it. His face broke into a wide grin. 'Gramps, you've been at it again. Preaching all that nonsense! This must be Mr. Gullible, if he's been brainwashed into believing that pack of old wives' tales.'

I looked down at his amused face, and felt suddenly angry. It must have shown on my face, because Paul immediately redoubled his efforts to embarrass me. He was obviously enjoying the chance to show off in front of his younger friend, and I was worried for Louise — I suspected that she was the person he really wanted to show off to. Mr. Westbury spoke quietly but firmly. 'Paul, I won't have you speak to my guests in that fashion.' He crossed the room to stand at my side. 'What you think about Christianity is your own affair. Kindly leave other people to make their own minds up.'

His quiet authority was like a bucket of cold water thrown over the bragging teenager, who immediately began to sulk. He said no more as Louise and I got ready to go.

'Remember,' said the judge as we walked past the two gleaming motor-bikes towards my Honda, 'Get involved with a lively church where you can start to grow and learn about God's word. You'll find a lot of people like Paul, I'm afraid, who'll try to pull you down and rob you of your faith. But you're lucky. Louise will stand by you. You were right, Tom. She's a fine Christian girl,'

Louise was talking with Mrs. Westbury and didn't

hear. Soon her head was snuggled against my shoulders as we rode to her home.

Her parents were just getting into their car. I was embarrassed. I'd never got on particularly well with either of them; I could sense they weren't happy that I was so obviously in love with their daughter, though they'd never said as much.

'Are you coming to church tonight, darling?' her mother called out, as Louise ran towards the car. The throb of the engine prevented me hearing the conversation but I could see their faces and I knew what she was telling her parents. Mrs. Dobson emerged from the car, ran over to me and threw her arms round my neck. She almost knocked me off my bike.

'I'm so *pleased*!' she bubbled.

Her father switched the engine off and strode across. 'Reckon I misjudged you, Tom,' he said. He stuck his hand out. It was a gesture of friendship. 'Come on — why don't we all go to church together, to celebrate?'

The idea of celebrating in church amused me. I briefly visualised glasses chinking under stained glass windows. 'Yes, that's great,' I said.

Ten minutes later I was sitting in unfamiliar wooden pews, surrounded by ladies in coats and men in suits. I was surprised to see a bunch of teenagers sitting together. I recognised an old school friend who was now at college. I had a look round for my mother, too, but I couldn't see her.

As I sat thumbing through the hymnbook and reading the text on the wall for the twentieth time, three women and two men came through the doors on either side of the pulpit and stood together. I couldn't work out what on earth they were up to. The women were wearing white gowns, and the men wore open-necked shirts and their feet were bare. I turned in bewilderment to Louise. 'Whatever are they up to?' I whispered.

'They're candidates for baptism,' she whispered back.

'I thought baptism was for babies!'

'This is a bit different,' she explained. 'They are new believers, who are going to join the church. They're obeying the Lord in baptism.'

I didn't understand what she meant by 'obeying the Lord', but before I could ask further, a surprisingly young man climbed into the pulpit and announced the first hymn. My eyes widened when, instead of an organ, a piano and guitar struck up the accompaniment. This wasn't what church was supposed to be like, in my book!

> From the rising of the sun
> To the going down of the same
> The Lord's name is to be praised . . .

There was a good beat to the tune; hands were waving, some clapped. People were smiling as they sang, joyfully. But — hadn't I always thought of church as a place where people had miserable faces?

> Praise ye the Lord!
> Praise him all ye people of the Lord
> Praise the name of the Lord . . .

After the hymn the minister said, 'We'll have a time of prayer.' I bowed my head, but nearly jerked it up again when several people started to pray, one after the other, just talking to God; they didn't follow any set pattern of praying, either; no special set of words, but speaking like two people might speak to each other. There weren't any 'thee's and thou's', nor were there in the reading from the Bible that followed. And when the sermon was preached it was as punchy and up-to-date as the morning paper.

I was still digesting all these revelations when the white-robed ladies and barefoot men got up, one after the other, and spoke. The minister said they were going to give their 'testimonies'. Apparently, giving a testimony was just talking about how you became a Christian. 'I was just aimless,' said one, 'drifting through life . . .'

'I got to a point where it all made sense,' said one of the men. 'If Jesus Christ had died for me then the only thing I could do in response was to give my life to him!' I nodded in agreement, and thought how crazy this would have sounded a week ago.

The other man was barely audible as he whispered the story of how he'd been a gambler for more than twenty years. And now God had saved him, just as he was about to lose his wife and his home.

A girl of Louise's age told how a fellow student had introduced her to Christ after she had been searching for an answer while at school. And the last said she had always believed, but now wanted to let the world know about it.

One at a time they descended the steps into a pool let into the floor, like a tiny swimming bath below the pulpit. I craned my neck to see. The minister asked his questions in a strong, clear voice.

'Do you believe in the Lord Jesus Christ as your personal Saviour? Are you trusting him and him alone for your salvation?'

'Yes!'

'And do you promise to follow him all the days of your life in the power of the Holy Spirit?'

'I do!'

'And because you so believe, you wish now to be baptised?'

'Yes!'

'Then on your good confession of faith I baptise you in the name of the Father, the Son and the Holy Spirit. Amen.'

Swoosh!

Right under the water.

As each one rose, dripping, he laid his hand on their head and prayed that God would give them power and direction by the Holy Spirit. The congregation burst into song:

> Who is on the Lord's side?
> Who will serve the King?
> Who will be his helper?

The minister held up a hand to halt the singing for a moment. 'Anybody here tonight who wants to become a Christian, or who wants to be baptised, is very welcome to come forward to the front of the church now.'

I felt suddenly hot and embarrassed. Louise, sensing it, squeezed my hand reassuringly. Her mother caught my eye and smiled at me; her father kept his eyes to the front and allowed his deep baritone full throttle as the minister waved us on to the next verse. My legs suddenly felt like lead weights.

> He whom Jesus nameth
> Must be on his side . . .

The words were oldfashioned, but I had no difficulty understanding them. I was now somebody who named Jesus, and I was going to be on his side. I found myself leaving my seat and walking up the aisle, to where the minister stood, his hand stretched out to welcome me.

8
Intensive care

It was late when I arrived home. I'd stayed behind after the service; Louise had introduced me to some of the young people. Then we'd gone on to the home of the youth leader, where there was a discussion about the problems of communicating Christianity to other people who didn't believe in it. Everybody admitted, they found it the hardest part of being a Christian. It wasn't that they weren't enthusiastic. One sixteen-year old had summed up everybody's feelings when she said, 'I want to tell my friends — but I just don't know how.'

I just don't know how — I thought about that all the way home. I'd only just started out as a Christian. But how was *I* to begin telling other people about Jesus? Mr. Westbury had told me — but he'd used a fast car and a hundred and fifty quid! I really wanted to know how to share what I'd found. It was the most incredible thing that ever happened to me.

As I let myself in the front door and tiptoed upstairs, my mother called down, 'Is that you, Tom?'

She came out of her bedroom clutching a piece of paper in her hand, looking more worried than usual.

'Whatever's the matter, Mum?'

'There's been a phone call for you, Tom. A Mrs. Westbury. She said you would want to know that her husband was admitted to the General Hospital Intensive Care Unit this evening. He's had a heart attack.'

My own heart pounded, I could feel it throbbing as I stood on the landing shocked and motionless. I couldn't believe the news. Only that morning I'd seen him striding energetically along with his dog by his side. There must have been a mistake — for a moment I wondered, crazily, whether this was some stupid practical joke of Mum's. But her face said it all. It wasn't a joke.

'I've got to go and see him,' I muttered, turning to go downstairs.

'Don't,' pleaded Mum. 'His wife won't want you getting in the way, not at a time like this. He's nothing to you. You leave his family to do what's needed. They'll not thank you . . .'

I ran downstairs, ignoring her pleas, slammed the door after me and ran to my Honda. I clenched my fist and slammed it into the taut leather of the pillion seat, and looked angrily at the stars overhead.

'Why, God? Why? Why? *Why?*'

I rammed my helmet onto my head and kicked the bike into life. I roared into the night, arrived at the hospital, and found the Unit, only to be told to come back in the morning. 'Mr. Westbury is unconscious,' the Sister said firmly. 'He can't have visitors tonight. Come back tomorrow.' It was no use arguing. I went back home.

I couldn't sleep. My anger at God subsided into a dreary sadness and a fear about what might happen to Mr. Westbury.

I got up early and rang Louise. I told her everything. 'Meet me at the Hospital,' I urged her. 'Take time off work — manage it somehow, Louise — you don't know how much I need you.'

I met her outside the glass doors of the Intensive Care Unit. A nurse saw us. 'Only close family, I'm afraid,' she said. 'No visiting yet.'

'I've got to see him,' I demanded. I realised I was

almost crying, but it didn't seem to matter. But the nurse was adamant. 'It's for his benefit,' she insisted. We turned away dejectedly, and met Mrs. Westbury coming up the corridor.

A few words from her to the nurse did the trick. Within five minutes we were allowed into Mr. Westbury's cubicle where he lay, his chest exposed, wires plastered into place. An oxygen cylinder stood by his bed, like a sentinel on guard. We had been there a few minutes before he sighed and opened his eyes. A look of pleasure crossed his face when he saw us.

'Darling!' he whispered. 'And Tom — and Louise — how kind of you to come.'

'Sister says you'll be fine,' his wife blurted out. It was hard to know which of them she was trying hardest to convince. Mr. Westbury smiled at her.

'Yes, I dare say . . . I'm in good hands here, you know. I don't think this one was as bad as the other.' He looked at me. 'Tom, old boy, it looks as though God wants you to take my place. You have come to a new birth, and I must face the end. Oh! it's all right — Margaret knows that this dicky heart of mine can't last much longer. I've been on borrowed time. There's only one thing I've prayed and longed for that hasn't come about, and that's that Paul will come to the Lord. He's been rather spoilt, I'm afraid.'

I couldn't help but agree with him. Paul, I reckoned, was the most unlikeable person I'd ever come across. I kept my opinions to myself as Mr. Westbury continued. 'I've tried to share my faith with him. But he's headstrong. He's wasting this year before college, and if he isn't careful he'll waste his whole life.'

'Why do you worry about him?' I burst in hotly. 'He doesn't care for you. He wouldn't talk to you like he does if he cared an ounce for you.'

He grinned as if in agreement, but added, 'Paul has had the gospel explained to him, but he seems incapable of understanding it. His attitude is just self-defence. He's using it to build a big barrier. I think you could break through that barrier, Tom.'

I'd like to break through his head, I thought to myself as I remembered how he'd showed off. My face must have shown what I was thinking; Mr. Westbury looked at me thoughtfully. 'When you can love him, Tom, you'll find a way. I know you will.'

He was becoming very drowsy. He stopped speaking and just nodded as we spoke to him. Soon his eyes drooped shut. A nurse came in, and looked at him. 'He's asleep now,' she said. 'Everybody except Mrs. Westbury must leave now, please.'

We left her sitting by her husband's side. I put my arm round Louise and held her tight. 'God's got a funny way of showing his gratitude,' I grunted through clenched teeth. 'That old man did everything to get me into heaven, and now look what's happened. I reckon he's on the way out — and that blasted grandson of his stands to get everything except his faith!'

'You're wrong, Tom,' whispered Louise. 'He only demonstrated to you what Christ did. A hundred and fifty pounds isn't the same as dying on a cross. And if you think Mr. Westbury is on the way out you're very much mistaken. On the way *up*, maybe; but not on the way *out*.'

She kissed me gently. I clung to her. After a moment or two we walked back towards the unit. Through the glass doors we could see the Sister comforting a tearful Mrs. Westbury. We realized immediately what had happened. We were too late. That trim moustache would not twitch any more to the excitement of life.

'I'll drive you home to Cadnam,' I said, taking Mrs.

Westbury's arm. She nodded silently. We found the blue Peugeot. She sat in that same seat in which I had first heard the message of God's love. The memories flooded back as I switched on the ignition.

Louise sat in the back seat and rested her hand on the motionless widow's shoulder.

When you can love him, Tom, you'll find a way. I know you will. His words came back into my mind as his car purred along towards the cottage in the forest. I suddenly realised what it was all about. Mr. Westbury had found a way with me because he'd loved me. Hadn't I been just as rude and argumentative as Paul? Yet he went on loving me and eventually finding a way through my thick skull. *That's it,* I decided. *I've got to find a way of reaching Paul. His grandfather's prayers mustn't go unanswered. But how? How can I even get to speak to him, let alone say the right things?*

I would have to write down everything I could remember of what Mr. Westbury had told me, I decided. Then I'd know what to say when the time came, to Paul and to others like him. There has to be a way of telling people my age about what happened to me. *And I will find it,* I promised myself — and Mr. Westbury.

We drove up to the cottage and I stopped the car. Mrs. Westbury turned to me with a smile. 'Thank you, Tom. And thank you for bringing Bertie so much happiness.' She looked at me appraisingly. 'You know, I think he has passed something of himself over to you.'

9
Death brings New Life

The funeral was to take place a week later. I spent every spare minute beforehand going over the gospel with Louise, who had collected every tract and pamphlet she could find. We decided that most of them were just too old-fashioned for sharing with people our age, but we found three of them very helpful: *Just grace, Journey into life*, and one called *Becoming a Christian*.

My only chance of speaking to Paul would be at the funeral; I would have to learn all I could in a week. I set to, learning the Bible verses quoted in the three books. Louise, who knew many of them already, tested me on the ones she thought were most important. We decided to use the booklet *Just grace* as our guide, partly because it set things out in a clear, easy-to-follow way, and partly because it reminded us of the way Mr. Westbury had explained things.

The night before the funeral was a Sunday, and at the youth fellowship we tried out what we had learned on the others. Louise was our spokesman.

'The first thing you have to realise is that heaven is a free gift. You don't deserve it, and you can't earn it by being good. The Bible says "It is by grace you have been saved through faith — and this is not from yourselves, it is the gift of God — not by works, so that no one can boast!"'

'What's "grace", Louise?' interposed the youth leader, pretending to be confused. Louise paused, trying to think of the best way of putting it.

'Grace? Well, it's kindness. It's getting something

you haven't deserved.'

'Uh, it's like hitch-hiking,' I chipped in. 'You stand at the roadside with your thumb held out. You haven't earned a lift — you don't pay for it — if somebody stops for you it's out of the kindness of their own heart.' I had to stop there, because the memory of my own trip to Oxford flooded back. Louise took over from me.

'OK, everyone,' she ordered, 'hold out your thumb as though you're thumbing a lift.' There was a lot of giggling as a forest of waving hands arose, each with thumb extended.

'Now,' she said, 'I've had an idea. Look at your hands. Now think of the gospel. There are five main aspects to it — grace, man, God, Christ, faith. Five aspects. Now, look at your hand. Get it?'

'Five fingers!' somebody called out. Louise beamed.

'Right! We're all carrying our own personal visual aid with us!'

We all began talking about Louise's idea, and the more we thought about it the more we liked it. Using our fingers as a sort of real-life diagram, we could remember what each of the points were that we had to talk about; we'd know where we were going. The thumb, which we used in hitch-hiking, would stand for God's grace, just as we'd been discussing it. Then, 'Man is a sinner!' — we'd hold up the index finger, to show that man's sin is that he goes his own way instead of God's. The next finger is the biggest, so we'd use that to represent God. And the Bible talked about the church as the bride of Christ — so what better to remind us of him than the ring finger? And finally, to complete the Bible's teaching, we could use the little finger to represent faith. A complete, ready-made guidebook to the gospel — right there on the end of of our arm.

'We've got it!' cried Louise. 'Tom, this means we've

got a way of sharing out faith with Paul — it might really help him to grasp it.'

We all prayed together, and especially for Paul, that the funeral would make him see things in a new light, and that Louise and I would have the opportunity to speak to him about Jesus.

The little Methodist Chapel was packed with mourners. From where we were sitting we could see the coffin, resting on its wooden trestles. A single spray of flowers lay on top.

The minister read the lesson. 'In my Father's house are many rooms. If it were not so, I would have told you. I am going there to prepare a place for you. And if I go and prepare a place for you, I will come back and take you to be with me, that you also may be where I am.'

Paul was sitting between Mrs. Westbury and his mother. He was wearing a dark blue suit, and looked serious and quiet.

Love divine, all loves excelling
Joy of heaven to earth come down
Fix in us thy humble dwelling
All thy faithful mercies crown.

Voices raised in heartfelt praise, as if to drown out any thought of sadness. *Just as the old man would have liked it,* I thought.

At the graveside, thirty or so mourners bowed their heads as the coffin slowly descended into the earth and the sombre, though joyous, words were repeated:

Earth to earth,
ashes to ashes,
dust to dust;
in the sure and certain
hope of the resurrection.
In the name of the Father
in the name of the Son
and of the Holy Spirit.
Amen.

Paul's father led his mother past the sprays and wreaths lining the pathway. Paul stood at the graveside looking down at the oak coffin with its single spray of flowers. There was a look on his face which might have been nervousness. He looked up. Our eyes met. Louise squeezed my arm encouragingly and went over to him.

'Hello, Paul.' She always knew the right way to speak to people; he responded visibly to her sympathy. An awkward smile appeared, and he gnawed his lip, holding back tears.

I think you could break through that barrier, Tom. The words of his grandfather — almost the last words he'd spoken — came back to me forcibly. I moved closer and stuck out my hand.

'I'm sorry, Paul.'

He turned his back without a word and walked to the waiting funeral car. I was scarlet-faced from the snub. I moved uncertainly after him, but before I had gone more than a few paces the door of his car slammed shut.

Louise slipped her arm through mine and led me back to the flowers and the hubbub of relatives talking.

I looked back at the black limousine turning out through the cemetery gates.

I had failed.

I hadn't broken the barrier.

10
An unexpected visitor

When we arrived home, Dad was still at work and Mum was busy with the washing. Louise and I sat without talking, occupied with our thoughts. The silence was eventually broken by Mum's cheery 'Who's for a cup of tea, then?'

Soon the three of us were talking over the events of the past nine days.

'I am glad you've started coming to church, Tom,' said Mum. 'I told you he was a nice minister, didn't I?'

'Yes, he was all right — what he said made a lot of sense . . . but it was Mr. Westbury who put it all together for me, Mum. I just wish I could have kept my promise and passed it on to Paul.'

'Maybe that's a good thing.'

'What do you mean?'

'Well, what could you possibly have said, after only two visits to church?'

I wasn't deterred. 'I'd have shared the hitch-hiker's guide to heaven with him, Mum. Yes, the hitch-hiker's guide to heaven would have made it plain, wouldn't it, Louise?'

Louise agreed. Mum raised her eyebrows.

'What on earth is the hitch-hiker's guide to heaven?'

'It's a way we worked out to tell other people like us about Jesus.'

'Well, why don't you try it out on me?' she suggested. 'I'll tell you soon enough whether it's any good!'

I looked at Louise; she nodded enthusiastically. I cleared my throat. It seemed a bit odd talking to my own mother like this, but I ploughed on.

'OK, Mum,' I began. 'First you have to answer some questions.'

She sat back and folded her arms.

'I'm ready.'

'If you died tonight, what would happen to you?'

She shifted uneasily on her chair and a worried frown crossed her face.

'I don't know,' she admitted.

'Well,' said Louise, 'would you go to heaven, for instance?'

'I hope so!'

'Yes,' I continued, stumbling a little, 'but do you have any *reason* for believing you will?'

'Well — I've always been a good mother, you know that . . . and I've done what I believed to be right . . . but anyway, where does the hitch-hiker bit come in?'

'You remember on the Friday before last I hitched to Oxford?'

'I should think I do!'

'I was standing by the side of the road and all the lorries and cars were going by. I was soaking wet and they didn't stop until Mr. Westbury did. Now: I hadn't done anything for Mr. Westbury. Just stuck my thumb out, begging for a little kindness. When he stopped, he did it out of the kindness of his heart, not because of anything I'd done to make him stop. And Mum, that's the only way anybody's going to get to heaven — just by the kindness of God. He gives it to us as a free gift. "The wages of sin is death, but the gift of God is eternal life." And this thumb reminds us.' I held it up. 'Heaven's a free gift. We don't deserve it and we can't earn it.'

I raised my index finger. Mum was leaning forward intently, following the argument.

'This finger says "I'm number one! God created me and has first claim on me — but I've rejected his authority, I want to live my own way!" The Bible calls that sin, and we're all guilty of it. "All have sinned, and fall short of the glory of God." ' I looked around. 'There are three of us sitting here — and by our own standards we could judge who is best and who worst, but as far as God is concerned it doesn't matter. "Whoever keeps the whole law and yet stumbles at just one point is guilty of breaking all of it." So man is a sinner — he can't save himself.'

I raised my middle finger. 'Look, Mum. The middle finger is bigger than all the others. That's a reminder that God is greater than man. He can love more than men can and he is more just than men are. He doesn't want to punish us, because he loves us. The Bible says, "He is patient with you, not wanting anyone to perish." But because God is just, he has to punish sin. That's what he says in the Bible: "I will punish the world for its evil and the wicked for their sin." That sounds like a contradiction, right? But look how God deals with it.'

I stuck my ring finger out with the others. I wasn't used to this exercise, and I had to hold my little finger back to stop it joining the others. 'OK, Mum. This is the ring finger, isn't it? And you know what rings stand for. Love. The Bible says, God loves us: "God so loved the world that he gave his one and only Son, that whoever believes in him shall not perish but have everlasting life." And God came into our world as the Lord Jesus Christ, lived a perfect life, and still died like any criminal.' I was getting excited just telling somebody else. And Mum seemed to be drinking it in. I continued:

'Remember how Dad just couldn't understand why a magistrate would pay my fine? All Mr. Westbury was doing was to teach me a lesson I'll never forget. I was guilty; he took the rap for me. And that's exactly what Jesus did for me. He was innocent, but he died for our sins. He took our place. When he did that, he did everything that the law demanded. The penalty was paid — in full! And at the same time, he was showing love to me. So love and justice were brought together. "God demonstrates his own love to us in this; while we were yet sinners Christ died for us." That was a verse Mr. Westbury told me.'

I spread my hand out, thumb and four fingers now erect. 'So that brings us to the little finger. And that reminds us that though our faith might be small, as small as a tiny mustard seed, that's all God is looking for. A faith that trusts him for what he has done. By faith we believe and put our trust in Christ. Faith is the arm that reaches out to receive the gift God is giving us.' I stopped, breathless. I'd done it. I'd explained the hitch-hiker's guide to heaven — God's plan of salvation. I looked cautiously at Mum. 'Did that make any sense at all?'

She looked at me as if stunned. Then she turned to Louise. 'Did you teach him that?'

Louise grinned at us. Mum turned back to us. 'Is that it? Is there any more?'

I couldn't tell what she thought of what she'd heard, so I plunged on. Extending my other hand, I continued.

'That was the hitch-hiker's guide to heaven, Mum. But like any guide, it's no use unless you use it. So the other hand shows what follows.' I held up my other thumb. 'This thumb says, "OK, I believe. I want to put my trust in Christ." And the next finger is the pointing finger. Remember, Mum? When I was a kid you had a poem you used to tell us — something about Tom Thumb and Peter Pointer . . .'

Mum nodded and smiled broadly.

'Well, Mum, Peter Pointer says, "Up to now I've been living life my way." God says — "Repent." That means, turn round from your sin, your "self-life", and start living the "Christ-life". It's like doing a U-turn when you realise you're heading in the wrong direction.' I stuck the next finger out. 'And the middle finger reminds us again, God is greater than we are. The Bible says "Jesus Christ is Lord," so he has the right to control our lives and make good use of us. I was a bit afraid of that until last week,' I added, 'until I understood that God has a plan for our lives. If he really loves me he'll show me how to live for him. And besides, you see this next finger — it reminds us about the Holy Spirit, who gives us the faith to believe, the desire to repent and the power to live for Jesus. The Holy Spirit gives us the new life which makes us God's children. And that reminds me. The last finger, the little one, shows that I come into God's family as a new-born baby. We're born again by the Spirit of God into God's family, the church. That's why I went to church last week, Mum. I wasn't trying to please Lou or anyone else. I just knew; I belonged there.'

Louise reached across and squeezed my hand. My mouth felt dry. No more words would come. I looked at Mum helplessly. She stared back. Her voice was a whisper.

'God gave you that, Tom.' A tear welled up in her eye and trickled slowly down her cheek. 'What must I *do*, son?'

I found my voice. 'Just believe, Mum. Believe, and ask God to give you eternal life.'

Another tear followed the first. Louise put her arm round Mum's shoulders and asked her if she wanted to pray.

'How come I never saw it before?' asked Mum. Her

voice was trembling. 'Of course I'll pray. But what?'

Upstairs was one of the booklets we'd been using. In it was a prayer. I ran upstairs to find it. By the time I came down again Mum had decided to pray in her own words.

'Father,' she said, 'I've been a fool. I've been going to church week after week, year in and year out, thinking I was a Christian. Now I know I wasn't. No wonder I've been living in fear. Please forgive me. I want your love and your gift of life. Please give me eternal life. I'm trusting you now and I want to live for you. Thank you, Father, thank you.'

We huddled together, our heads bowed. As she finished there was silence. We heard a key turning in the front door. All three of us raised our heads. Mum went to the cupboard to get another cup. Before she got back to the teapot Dad had reached the kitchen. He looked at each of us in turn. He obviously knew something was happening. A frown rested on his forehead. 'Whatever's the matter, woman?' he asked Mum, without any unkindness.

Mum smiled nervously. 'I've just become a Christian, Freddie.'

He looked startled, and his curiosity turned to laughter.

'You've done *what*?'

'I'm a Christian too, Dad,' I said.

He sat down heavily and stared at Louise. Then he shook his head doubtfully and rested his chin on his hand. 'Listen, boy. You've had a shock, what with Westbury dying and all that. I'm sorry about what I said after the court case. I shouldn't have said what I did about him. It just seemed odd, that's all. I think what he did was blooming marvellous, but in all honesty I don't understand what you're talking about. Your

Mum's always been religious; I've done nothing to stop her. And if that's what you two young 'uns want, who am I to stop you? Just don't expect me to change. I'm an old dog, I've seen too much of life to start changing now.' He clapped Mum on the shoulders. 'Come on, then, Lil. Let's get tea under way.'

I looked at Mum. She was smiling. I knew it wasn't the end of the matter for Dad. Mum wouldn't let it be.

We went upstairs and gathered all our notes and booklets. 'Let's get this really pulled together,' said Louise, 'so that we can give it to other Christians to help them share their faith. Who knows? One of us might be the one that reaches Paul with the message of the man who paid the penalty for all our sin.'

We picked up the last of the papers and went downstairs to tea and Mum and Dad.

The following pages are written in the hope that you will find the same faith and share it with your friends.

The Hitch-hiker's Guide
to Heaven
Self-help Manual

A word from the author

The novel you have just read may have brought you to faith in Christ or confirmed what you already knew and believed. It is my hope that it has also stirred you to share your faith with others. Your church may want to adopt the *Teach and Reach* training programme devised by Evangelism Explosion (228 Shirley Road, Southampton, SO1 3HR). But you as an individual can make a start by using the remainder of this book as a do-it-yourself kit in evangelism. I suggest you take time to learn each of the finger points and then add to each of them Scriptures and illustrations. I have provided some by way of example. You may like to start with these and build on others as you come across them in your daily reading.

PRESENTATION OUTLINE

Getting Started
Pray.
Relate.
Ask questions.
Your testimony.

Presenting the Gospel
Hitcher's Thumb —
I'm number one.
Two sides of God.
Christ and cross.
Have faith.

What's Involved
Trusting Christ alone.
Repenting of sin.
Under New Management.
Spirit's work.
The Living Church.

New Life
Pray to receive.
Read John 6:47.
Ask assurance question.
Year contract.

GETTING STARTED

Pray

Any man-made method of presenting the Gospel is bound to fail unless it is offered to God to be used by him. John 3:6 reminds us that, 'Flesh gives birth to flesh but the Spirit (of God) gives birth to the spirit.' If we work and struggle in our own strength by using clever arguments and manipulate people by clever 'sales techniques' we shall get nowhere. Obviously, as you have seen in the novel, a clear presentation of the truth is essential; but only the Spirit can take that and use it to give birth to the spirit. You have been called – like the early disciples – into a working partnership with the Holy Spirit. Jesus said to them (Acts 1:8), 'You will receive power when the Holy Spirit comes to you; and you will be my witnesses.' For these men, the art of telling others about Jesus was out of the question if divorced from prayer. (Acts 6:4).

Start now:

- ■ Pray for yourself, that you may learn this presentation.
- ■ Make a list of friends and family who need to hear the gospel and pray for them specifically.
- ■ Find a Christian friend who will pray for you regularly. Show him Colossians 4:3 and ask him if he will become your prayer partner.
- ■ Pray that God will help you to meet others who need to hear the gospel from you.

Relate

Did you notice from the story of Tom how important a good relationship was? It is a fact that no-one will accept what you have to say until they have first accepted you.

71

Their sub-conscious mind will question your integrity, doubt your understanding and challenge your version of the truth because, 'The god of this age [Satan] has blinded the minds of unbelievers, so that they cannot see the light of the gospel' (2 Corinthians 4:4). You may know a person for a period of many years and yet have zero relationship. On the other hand you may meet a person for the first time and establish an instant rapport. Some people will be attracted to you because of the kind of person you are. Indeed, the more you live for Christ the more attractive you are. Love comes from 'a pure heart and a good conscience and a sincere faith' (1 Tim. 1:5).

With some folk you will need to spend time building a bridge of relationship, before presenting the gospel. If you rush into the hitch-hiker's guide they may resent you and close their ears to what you are saying. Or worse still, you will find yourself arguing the point. Remember, it's very difficult to be hostile with a friend.

Reach Out or Draw In
Having established the principle of relationship evangelism and praying for divine appointments you will recognise the need to make an initial contact. Sometimes this will be a reaching-out operation. 'I chose you to go and bear fruit' (John 15:16). You will want to draw up a list of places where young people congregate, such as school, college, disco, sports facilities, clubs, etc. These are primary targets for evangelistic outreach. Sometimes you can create situations into which other young folk can be drawn as a point of contact. When you have learned the hitchhiker's guide you may find that an occasional coffee-bar, camp or weekend away with a small group creates just the right environment for relationships to be built. Ask God to make you creative

in establishing many meeting-points. Keep your eyes open too for all those natural openings among your regular friends and family.

Ask Questions

Once you have contact with any individual you are going to be faced with the challenge of making the transition between ordinary conversation to presenting the gospel. I have found that the best way of doing this is to ask the relevant questions such as:–

Do you ever go to church? Most people who do not go to church will immediately give you reasons why they don't. Often these are ill-informed, preconceived prejudices such as, 'The church is full of hypocrites, the services are dull and boring or just not for young people.' You do not have to go on the defensive or become argumentative. Gently admit where the failures are and share your own positive experience as a testimony. You will often be able to tell from the response to this one question whether a person is a Christian or not and whether they are interested in pursuing the subject further.

Why are we here? Many times this is the most puzzling question for young people. Why are we alive on this planet? What's the difference between men and the animals? What's your purpose in life? It can be asked in so many ways and has a multitude of answers each one of which is an opening for your own testimony of the new life you have found in Christ.

What happens to us when we die? Most young folk have not given this too much thought unless they have faced death themselves or lost someone very close. But the question itself has a remarkable impact and again gives a tremendous opening for your personal testimony.

If you died and stood before God and he said to you,

'Why should I let you into my heaven?' what would you say?

This question enables you to zero in on what the person is trusting in already. He may plead that he doesn't know, in which case you can ask him if he would like you to share how you came to know you have eternal life. He is most likely to say that he hopes he's good enough (i.e. good works). Occasionally you may find a person honest enough to admit he is not good enough. Very few young people attach any significance to their baptism as babies or confirmation, unless they are actually believers; but very occasionally you may have someone answer, 'Because I go to church,' or 'Because I've been brought up in a Christian home.'

Whichever way they answer, again you have an opportunity for pressing on to your testimony.

Your Testimony

The questions you have asked have created a natural opening for you to share your own experience. Normally you can divide this into three parts.

- *What you were like before you believed.* You don't need to go into a lot of detail here especially if you were converted at a very early age. The only value in this section is to find a point of contact with your friend, which says, 'I understand you – I've been where you are today.'
- *How you became a Christian.* Avoid the use of clichés and religious jargon. Just give the facts simply, quickly and honestly.
- *What Christ has done for you.* The central point of your testimony is to show what Christ has done for you. He's given you a brand new life with peace, joy, satisfaction, love, acceptance,

purpose, self-control and above all assurance of eternal life.

As you are giving your testimony (which need last no longer than two or three minutes) keep an eye open for responsiveness and interest. Sometimes you will stop at this stage and wait for another opening, rather than bulldoze your way into the hitch-hiker's guide. If on the other hand your contact seems open to the gospel, ask him if you may share the main message of the Bible.

By way of introduction, you may explain that you have read this book and find it a useful aid to your memory to go through each of the finger points. This gives your listener something to latch on to, and even if he makes no immediate commitment he will be able to remember most of the points covered.

PRESENTING THE GOSPEL

1. Hitcher's Thumb

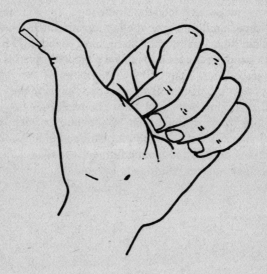

Heaven is a free lift – it is not a reward for work.

Most people believe that heaven is for people whose good points outweigh their bad. It is, therefore, important to break this preconceived notion with a clear statement of Scripture.

■ *Learn* Ephesians 2:8–9 'It is by grace (God's kindness) you have been saved, through faith, and this is not from yourselves, it is the gift of God – not by works so that no-one can boast.'

- **■** *Learn* Titus 3:5 'He saved us, not because of righteous things we had done, but because of his mercy.'
- **■** *Learn* Romans 6:23 'The *gift* of God is eternal life.'

Hold your thumb out in the motion of a hitch-hiker and explain that just as the lift by a kind motorist is free with no strings attached so God's gift of heaven is free, an act of his kindness.

2. I'm Number One

Use the index finger pointing upwards to illustrate

I did it my way.

Sin to many, is an old-fashioned word. In the common mind it has come to mean something really bad. So a sinner is almost synonymous with a criminal or at the very least someone who is habitually antisocial. The original meaning of the word needs to be re-captured. It means anything which stems from our rebellion against God's authority over our lives, i.e. 'I'm number one.' This rebellion is most easily recognised by self-centred behaviour which has varying degrees of acceptance and rejection within society. In God's eyes, however, we are all sinners.

■ *Learn* Romans 3:23 'For all have sinned and fall short of the glory of God.'

- *Learn* Colossians 1:21 'Alienated from God – enemies in your minds because of your evil behaviour.'
- *Learn* James 2:10 'Whoever keeps the whole law and yet stumbles at one point is guilty of breaking all of it.'
- *Illustration* If you know which sport your friend enjoys you can use it to illustrate sin as 'missing the mark', i.e. If a footballer kicks the ball at goal he may hit the cross-bar or shoot yards wide but it amounts to just the same – no goal. The same principle can be applied to most sports and make the point that some people may get close by not doing things which are sinful but may miss God's mark by leaving good things undone.
- *Learn* James 4:17 'Anyone, then, who knows the good thing he ought to do and doesn't do it, sins.'

3. Two sides of God's Nature

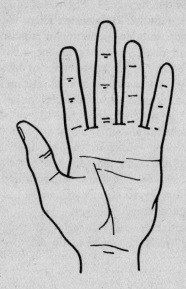

Show how the middle finger is larger than all the others to illustrate God's greatness over man.

God is Love (1 John 4:9).

Most people have no real problem with this statement of Scripture. Love is beneficial and benevolent. It is precisely because God loves us that we are given the gift of eternal life. He hates the sin but loves the sinner.

> ■ *Learn* 2 Peter 3:9 'He is patient with you, not wanting anyone to perish.' He does not want to punish us!

God is Just (Deuteronomy 32:4).

The same Bible tells us that the God who loves us and doesn't want to punish us will because he is just.

■ *Learn* Isiah 13:11 'I will punish the world for its evil and the wicked for their sins.'

■ *Learn* Romans 6:23 'The wages of sin is death.'

Tom's courtroom scene is an excellent illustration of how God overcomes an apparent contradiction by bringing love and justice together in one act. Unless you understand that God must be true to his nature and exercise fully his justice and love, and neither at the expense of the other, you will never convey the central truth of the gospel.

4. Christ and the Cross

The wedding ring finger illustrates the promise between two people to live together in love.

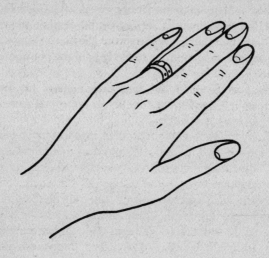

Christ

God brought his love and his justice together by coming into the world in the person of Christ. In other words Jesus was God in human form.

- ■ *Learn* Colossians 1:15 'He (Jesus) is the image of the invisible God.'
- ■ *Learn* Colossians 1:19 'For God was pleased to have all his fullness dwell in him.'
- ■ Colossians 2:9 'For in Christ all the fullness of the deity lives in bodily form.'
- ■ *Learn* John 14:9 'Anyone who has seen me has seen the Father.' As man, Jesus, lived a sinless life.
- ■ *Learn* Hebrews 4:15 'We have one (Jesus) who has been tempted in every way, just as we are — yet was without sin.'

The Cross

At the end of a sinless life Jesus was sentenced to death by crucifixion. Historically, the charge was one of blasphemy, that he claimed to be equal with God. This charge he never denied, for, as we have seen, he was God in human form. The Scripture shows us what was really happening upon the cross. He paid the penalty for our sin.

- ■ *Learn* Romans 5:8 'God demonstrates his own love for us in this: while we were still sinners Christ died for us.'
- ■ *Learn* Colossians 1:22 'But now he has reconciled you by Christ's physical body through death (on the cross) to present you holy in his sight, without blemish and free from accusation.' He died to deal with our sin and the third day he rose from the dead (proving that as God he is indestructible!). He ascended to heaven and from there offers the gift of forgiveness and eternal life.
- ■ *Learn* 1 Corinthians 15:21 'For since death came through a man (Adam) the resurrection of the dead also comes through a man. For as in Adam all die, so in Christ all will be made alive.'

5. Have Faith

Use the little finger to show that even if you have faith as small as a mustard seed it is enough to trust Christ's promise of eternal life. We receive this gift by faith. That is by beliving in what Christ has done for us on the cross.

- ◼ *Learn* John 3:16 'For God so *loved* the world that he *gave* his one and only Son, so that *whoever believes* in him shall not perish but have eternal life.'
- ◼ *Illustration* To show that faith must be an active response. If our hitch-hiker friend has a car stop to give him a lift he has a way of getting to his destination. But he still has to get into the car to go. It's no use just believing it can take him; he must trust himself to the driver who *will* take him.

■ *Learn* John 3:36 'Whoever believes in the Son has eternal life, but whoever rejects the Son will not see life, for God's wrath remains on him.'

WHAT'S INVOLVED?

On the one hand you have explained the nature of the Gospel simply and conversationally. You may have had many questions to answer along the way (see appendix for how to cope with common objections) but all the time you have been bringing your friend back to the message by using your fingers.

Before you ask your contact to make any commitment you can use your other hand to show what is involved.

1. Trusting Christ Alone

As we have seen there is nothing to stand in the place of Christ. Religion, whether formal traditionalism or primed with the pump of modern thinking or razz-a-ma-tazz, is of itself without Christ, empty and disappointing. Works, as we have seen in the gospel will not save anyone. No amount of money can buy it. Only trust in Christ is sufficient.

Thumbs up sign. 'O.K. I believe. I want to put my trust in Christ.'

- *Learn* Romans 9:33 'The one who trusts in him (Jesus) will never be put to shame.'
- *Learn* Philippians 3:9 'That I may gain Christ and be found in him, not having a righteousness of my own that comes from the law, but that which is through faith in Christ.'

2. Repenting of Sin

Which direction?

As we have already seen, sin is rebelling against God's authority and living the self life. Repentance is an act of faith which rejects the self life and starts living for God, the Christ life. It involves more than just turning over a new leaf for that would lead back to works. Repentance alone will not save! Repentance is the first act of belief.

■ *Learn* 2 Peter 3:9 'He is patient with you, not wanting anyone to perish, but everyone to come to repentance.'

3. Under New Management

Again the middle finger is the highest. Repentance leads to an acknowledgement that Jesus is Lord. This shows where good works come into the picture.

■ *Learn* Ephesians 2:10 'We are God's workman-
    ship, created in *Christ Jesus* to do good works,
    which God prepared in advance for us to do.'
In other words, we have returned by trusting Christ and
repenting of sin to God's plan for our lives. Jesus is the
focal point of that plan.

■ *Learn* John 14:23 'If anyone loves me, he will
    obey my teaching.'

4. Spirit's Work

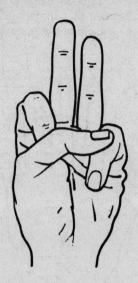

Keep your middle finger showing the Lordship of Christ and raise the one next to it to show that next to Christ is the Holy Spirit. God has sent his Holy Spirit to help us.

It is with his help that we trust Christ.

- ■ *Learn* Romans 8:16 'The Spirit himself testifies with our spirit that we are God's children.'
- ■ *Learn* John 3:6 'Flesh gives birth to flesh, but the Spirit gives birth to spirit.'

5. The Living Church

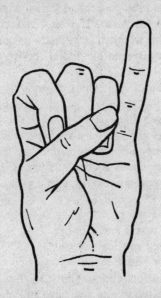

The little finger shows that whatever age your contact may be, in the eyes of God, he is a little child. If he puts his trust in Christ he will be 'born again – of the Spirit.'

- *Learn* John 1:12 'Yet to all who received him, to those who believe in his name, he gave the right to become the children of God.'

We are God's children and therefore members of his family.

- *Learn* Ephesians 2:19 'Consequently, you are no longer foreigners and aliens, but fellow citizens with God's people and members of God's household.'

NEW LIFE

You have shared the gospel and shown what is involved in becoming a Christian. If your contact seems to be positive ask him whether he is ready to put his trust in Jesus Christ and repent of sin and receive God's gift of eternal life.

If he is you can invite him to pray.

Pray to receive

Sometimes it is good to have the new believer pray his own prayer, but most young people are happier either reading a prayer from a booklet such as *Just Grace* or being led to repeat a phrase at a time using a prayer like this:—

Heavenly Father,
I confess that I am a sinner.
I have lived my life my way.
I am sorry and I repent of my sin.
Thank you for sending Christ to die in my place.
Please forgive me as you have promised.
Please give me your gift of eternal life.
I want to live for you from today on.
Help me by your Holy Spirit.
In Jesus name I pray.   Amen

After a suitable period of silence take your pocket testament.

Read John 6:47

■ *Learn* John 6:47 'I tell you the truth, he who believes has eternal life.'

Ask Assurance Question

It is very important to have your new Christian friend voice his own assurance. After you have read John 6:47

and explained the promise as a present possession, you may ask, 'On the basis of what is promised here do you have eternal life?' and 'Are you trusting Jesus Christ alone for your salvation?'

Year contract
When you have had the joy of seeing your friend become a Christian your responsibilities have only just begun. You may give this book as a present to confirm what has happened and repeat the cycle of initial training you have received. The booklet *Just Grace* available from your local Christian bookstore has been designed to point the way forward for the new Christian. Where possible you will want to spend time during the next year encouraging your new friend into the life of a lively church where the Bible is studied and Christians live for each other in the love of Christ.

Appendix: Handling Objections

'The god of this age (satan) has blinded the eyes of the unbelievers, so that they cannot see the light of the gospel of the glory of Christ.' 2 Corinthians 4:4. Though the individual objector may sincerely believe that his questioning springs from an intelligent search for truth, we should always remember that spiritual truth cannot be understood by human logic alone. Spiritual things are spiritually discerned.

When a person raises an objection, therefore, we should recognise it as part of satan's attempt to keep a person in spiritual blindness. Prayer is our weapon. Whenever an objection is raised, pray! 'Our struggle is not against flesh and blood . . . but against spiritual forces of evil.' God has placed at your disposal all the resources to meet even the most difficult situation. Your defence is the armour of God. Ephesians 6:13-18.

Verse 13, 'Stand your ground'. That does not mean to say you have to become beligerent and hostile. A rock may receive heavy pounding from the sea but it does not attack the sea. Every wave that crashes on the rock is forced to give way. When you put on God's armour you can stand firm. God's Armour.

1. Truth. (v.14). So long as you are truthful your integrity will shine through. Your contact may be objecting in order to throw up a smoke screen because he feels threatened by the gospel, which he knows will mean certain changes in his life. You do not have to pander to his fears and water down the gospel. The truth may sometimes hurt but it is also

the beginning of healing.

2. Righteousness. (v.14). If your righteousness is displayed in a superior, 'holier than thou' attitude it will only serve to create more hostility. However, if your behaviour and speech have been sancitified by God's grace (the righteousness of Christ), what you say will carry much more weight than if you try to beat down your contact's arguments with your own arguments.

3. Gospel of Peace. (v.15). It takes two to make an argument. If you are offering a gospel of peace with war-like methods you will certainly lose any confidence in your integrity which your contact may have had before you started reacting.

4. Faith. (v.16). If you have the faith, He has the power. Put your confidence in God the Holy Spirit to work in the objectors mind.

5. Salvation. Your own testimony and assurance will weigh more than a dozen objections to the gospel.

6. Word of God. You are not speaking on your own authority but from the Word of God. When answering any objection your first and last appeal is to the word of God. If you do not know what the word of God says on the subject do not try to substitute it by human logic. That will invariably fail.

7. Pray. God is with you to help you.

Four Ways of Handling Objections

1. Preclude. The best way to handle any objection is to answer it before it is raised. For example, we always talk about the love of God before His justice to preclude the objection, 'Oh! my God's not like that. My God is a God of love.'

2. Postpone. a. Until later in the presentation. Suppose

95

you are talking about 'grace' and your host asks you a question about 'Christ'. You can quickly acknowledge the question as being a relevant one which you will answer later and which will be clearer in the light of what you are presently saying.

b. Until after the presentation. If the question appears to be a smoke screen which has nothing to do with the presentation you may postpone answering it by saying something like, 'Tony, that's an interesting question and I'm sure we could have quite a discussion on that point. However, it doesn't seem to have much bearing on what you invited me to share with you. That is what the Bible says about how you can be sure about eternal life. Would you like me to continue what I was saying on the understanding that if when I have finished you would like to raise that question again you are free to do so?'

Often you will discover that a person will say 'Yes' to this and in the light of the complete gospel presentation, may not even want to raise the question again.

Sometimes a question may be asked out of sequence which though you are coming to it later, appears to have some urgency to it now. In which case, it is better to answer it immediately. What is out of sequence in the presentation as you have learned it may be in sequence in the live situation. Remember, the presentation is your tool not your master.

3. Quickly Answer. If you can accurately answer the question do so quickly and return to the presentation at the point at which you left it.

4. Research. If you do not know the answer to a particular question it does not hurt to admit your ignorance. After all you cannot be expected to know

everything. Often such an admission will warm you to your contact who will certainly have a greater respect for your integrity than if you try to bluff your way through with a phoney answer.

If, however, you believe there is an answer and that this is so important to your host that it appears to be the only stumbling block you may offer to either research it or bring a book or cassette recording on the subject for your host to consider.

Reprinted from Teach and Reach
by kind permission

Books which help you find an answer

Know Why you Believe Paul Little I.V.P.
Know What you Believe Paul Little I.V.P.
More than a Carpenter Josh McDowell Living Books
Evidence that Demands a Verdict Josh McDowell Here's Life Publishers
Why I believe D.J. Kennedy Marshall Morgan & Scott
Answers Josh McDowell Here's Life Publishers
Your must be Joking Michael Green Hodder & Stoughton
Follow-up
1. *Just Grace* Vic Jackopson Evangelism Explosion (GB) Ltd. Available: EE. (GB) Ltd. 228 Shirley Road, Southampton SO1 3HR
2. *Growing in Christ Book* Navigators (Naupress) Available: Scripture Press, Chiltern Avenue, Amesham-on-the-Hill, Bucks. HP6 5AX.
3. *Five Steps of Christian Growth* Campus Crusade for Christ. Available: Willard Thompson Ltd, Grafton Place, Worthing. BN11 1QX
4. *Every Day With Jesus* (New Christians Issue). Available: CWR, Box 11, Walton-on-Thames, Surrey.